the ultimate Hawaii activity book

THEMED GAMES, PUZZLES, COLORING & LEARNING FUN, PLUS A TRAVEL PLANNER, JOURNALING PAGES & PACKING LISTS FOR KIDS AGES 8 AND UP

BY NANCY J. PRICE & PRINTCOLORFUN.COM

FOR MORE COLORING PAGES, GAMES & MORE
VISIT PRINTCOLORFUN.COM

SEE MORE BOOKS AT PRINTCOLORFUN.COM

Find out more about these books, plus get hundreds of free printables online at PrintColorFun.com

A PRINT.COLOR.FUN! BOOK

THE ULTIMATE HAWAII ACTIVITY BOOK

Themed Games, Puzzles, Coloring & Learning Fun,
Plus a Travel Planner, Journaling Pages & Packing Lists for Kids Ages 8 and Up

A PrintColorFun.com Book

Images licensed via Adobe, Deposit Photos, Dreamstime, Envato, Freepik, Fotolia
and other sources, and many have been modified from their original designs.

Synchronista® is a registered trademark of Synchronista LLC

Published by PrintColorFun.com, a division of Synchronista LLC – Gilbert, Arizona, USA

Web: Synchronista.com | PrintColorFun.com

The Ultimate Hawaii Activity Book

In addition to all the coloring pages, puzzles and other fun inside, get packing lists & vacation journaling pages at the end of this book!

CONTENTS

10-week travel countdown	Page 4
Details about your Hawaiian vacation	Page 5
About Hawaii	Pages 6-9
Lots of puzzles, coloring pages & other fun	Pages 10-111
Packing list	Page 112
Checklists	Page 114
Travel journal pages	Page 117
Puzzle solutions	Page 125

KAUAI

Lihue

NIIHAU

OAHU

Wahiawa   Kaneohe

HONOLULU

Kalaupapa   MOLOKAI
Hoolehua

LANAI   Wailuku
Lanai City   Lahaina   MAUI   Hana

KAHOOLAWE

You're going to Hawaii!

Waimea

Hilo

Kailua-Kona   HAWAII

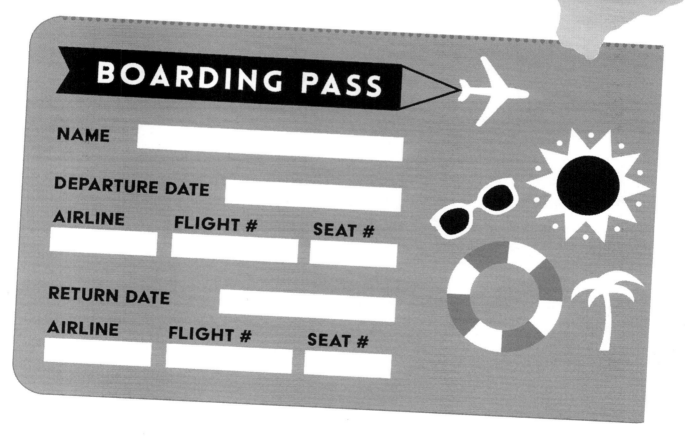

BOARDING PASS

NAME

DEPARTURE DATE

AIRLINE   FLIGHT #   SEAT #

RETURN DATE

AIRLINE   FLIGHT #   SEAT #

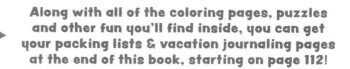

Along with all of the coloring pages, puzzles and other fun you'll find inside, you can get your packing lists & vacation journaling pages at the end of this book, starting on page 112!

10-WEEK TRAVEL COUNTDOWN

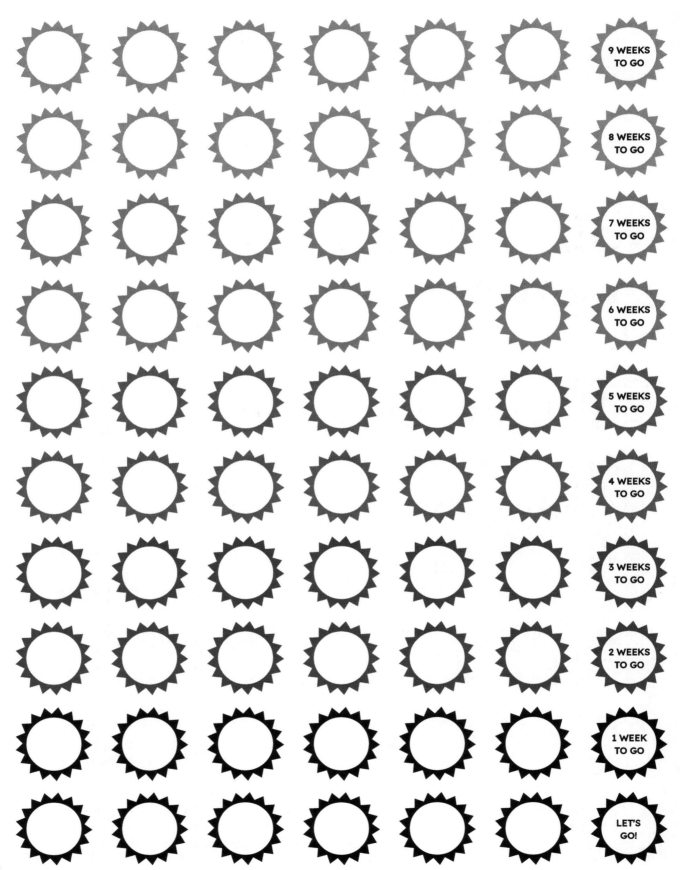

9 WEEKS TO GO

8 WEEKS TO GO

7 WEEKS TO GO

6 WEEKS TO GO

5 WEEKS TO GO

4 WEEKS TO GO

3 WEEKS TO GO

2 WEEKS TO GO

1 WEEK TO GO

LET'S GO!

ABOUT YOUR HAWAIIAN VACATION

WHEN THE TRIP BEGINS

DATE/TIME: SUN   MON   TUE   WED   THU   FRI   SAT

DETAILS:

WHERE YOU ARE GOING

WHEN YOU'RE RETURNING HOME

DATE/TIME: SUN   MON   TUE   WED   THU   FRI   SAT

DETAILS:

SEE PACKING LISTS & JOURNALING PAGES AT THE END OF THIS BOOK!

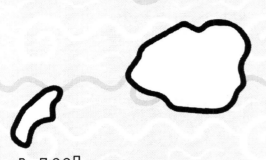

Kauai
"The Garden Isle"
Hawaiian: Kaua'i

Niihau
"The Forbidden Isle"
(Private island)
Hawaiian: Ni'ihau

Oahu
"The Gathering Place"
Hawaiian: O'ahu

This is Hawaii

Hawaii, America's 50th state, is located in the Pacific Ocean, more than 2,500 miles from the continental United States (in Hawaii, they call that "the mainland").

There are eight major islands, shown here: Hawaii, Maui, Oahu, Kauai, Molokai, Lanai, Niihau and Kahoolawe.

But the state doesn't stop with those eight! There are also the Northwestern Hawaiian Islands, a mostly uninhabited chain of more than 100 small islands and coral reefs *(atolls)* that run northwest of the main islands.

All of these volcanic islands are part of the same underwater mountain range. They were formed starting about 28 million years ago, and were still emerging from the ocean until around 400,000 years ago.

Hawaii is located in the South Pacific, and is part of Polynesia — meaning the islands within the Polynesian Triangle, a geographic area made by connecting Hawaii, New Zealand and Easter Island.

Molokai
"The Friendly Isle"
Hawaiian: Moloka'i

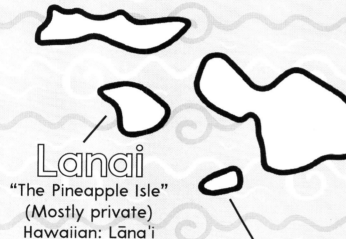

Maui
"The Valley Isle"
Hawaiian: Maui
(no okina)

Lanai
"The Pineapple Isle"
(Mostly private)
Hawaiian: Lāna'i

Kahoolawe
"The Target Isle"
(Uninhabited island
with restricted access)
Hawaiian: Kaho'olawe

Hawaii
"The Big Island"
Hawaiian: Hawai'i

7

HAWAII: FAST FACTS

Capital: Honolulu

Population: 1.416 million
(as of 2019)

Nickname: The Aloha State

Statehood: August 21, 1959

State flower: Yellow Hibiscus

State fish: Humuhumunukunukuapua'a

State bird: Nene (Hawaiian Goose)

State mammal: Monk Seal

Motto: Ua Mau ke Ea o ka 'Āina i ka Pono
("The life of the land is perpetuated
in righteousness")

Visitors per year: 7 million+

Distances from Honolulu:

To Los Angeles: 2,558 miles

To Seattle: 2,678 miles

To Tokyo: 3,854 miles

To Houston, Texas: 3,892 miles

To Chicago: 4,246 miles

To Columbus, Ohio: 4,500 miles

To New York City: 4,957 miles

To Sydney, Australia: 5,071 miles

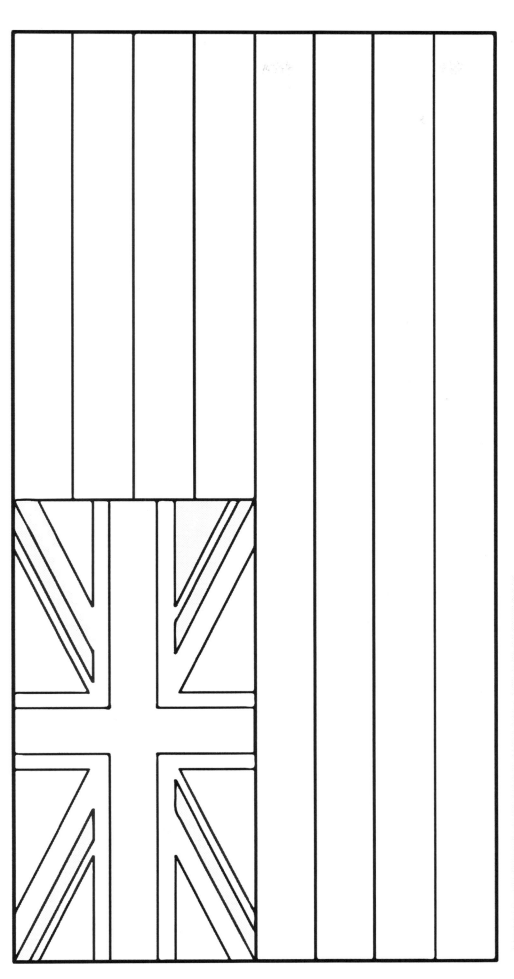

WAVE THE FLAG

Hawaii's state flag has 8 horizontal stripes, each one representing one of the major islands. From top to bottom, the stripes are white, red, blue, white, red, blue, white, red. On the upper left corner of the flag is the British Union Jack flag (a red cross in the middle, blue triangles, red diagonal lines and the outlines in white). The British flag was used in Hawaii during the late 1700s and early 1800s.

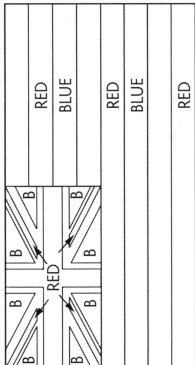

Tiki Time

A tiki — called *ki'i* in Hawaiian — is a wooden or stone carving that was originally used by the ancient Polynesians as a statue or a mask.

Most were made to look like one of the many old Hawaiian gods.

The tikis were said to have the spiritual power to do things like protect and strengthen people, grow healthy crops, and guard important places.

People still make tiki masks and sculptures today, but they're also seen on everything from T-shirts to coffee mugs.

Here, see how many tiki-style masks you can match up!

3 MATCHING TIKIS: FIND 8
2 MATCHING TIKIS: FIND 2
NON-MATCHING TIKI: FIND 1

Leis are thick strands of flowers and leaves sewn together and worn as necklaces or draped around the head.

The craft of lei-making stretches back throughout the history of Hawaii. Leis were often made from colorful, fragrant native flowers, including red lehua, white ginger, and yellow ilima.

Today, the most popular flowers for leis are plumerias, carnations and pikake. Orchids are popular with those who want a fragrance-free lei.

Leis are used to welcome others, whether they be strangers or friends; to celebrate holidays, weddings, and birthdays; and to honor the dead.

lovely leis

Sources: Office of Historian/US House of Representatives & National Endowments for the Arts

MEALS & WHEELS

Hawaii's beachside food trucks are well-known to local residents, surfers and even some adventurous tourists. You will find them serving Hawaiian favorites as well as dishes from many other countries. Be sure to keep an eye out for the shave ice truck, so you can get a fruity frozen treat! *(Yes, in Hawaii, it's "shave ice" not "shaved ice.")*

JUST A FEW OF THE FUN THINGS TO DO IN HAWAII

~~DANCE~~
~~EAT~~
~~HIKE~~
PADDLE
PARASAIL
~~PLAY~~
~~RUN~~
~~SAIL~~
~~SIGHTSEE~~
SNORKEL
SURF
SWIM
WALK

See solutions starting on page 125

E	L	D	D	A	P	T	H	S	B
H	P	L	N	D	A	S	W	I	M
V	S	A	T	E	Y	F	E	G	W
Y	N	T	R	A	R	K	C	H	N
T	O	S	L	A	I	U	H	T	T
C	R	P	U	H	S	L	N	S	D
H	K	T	B	R	J	A	M	E	R
M	E	T	P	L	F	Q	I	E	Q
X	L	T	D	A	N	C	E	L	V
C	K	L	A	W	T	S	A	I	L

13

Aloha
(uh-low-ha)
Hello or goodbye

Keiki
(kay-kee)
Child

Ohana
(oh-hana)
Family or neighborhood

Ono (oh-no)
Something tasty or good to eat

Wiki
(wick-ee)
Fast

Kāne
(kah-nay)
Man

Hula
(who-lah)
A traditional Hawaiian form of dance

Wahine
(wah-he-nee)
Woman

Luau
(loo-oww)
Hawaiian feast of celebration

Poi (like "boy")
A paste-like Hawaiian food made from the root of the taro plant

Mahalo
(mah-hallow)
Thank you

The Hawaiian alphabet

There are just 12 letters in the Hawaiian alphabet, so every word in the island's language is spelled using less than half of the English alphabet!

The letters of the island alphabet are shown below, and you'll see that they don't include B, C, D, F, G, J, Q, R, S, T, V, X, Y or Z.

• •

The letters are:

A = "ah"
E = "ey" or "ay"
I = "ee"
O = "oh"
U = "oo"
H, K, L, M, N, P, W

Also considered part of the alphabet is the ' symbol, called the **'okina**. This is a mark that means you should add a quick pause where it's inserted between letters, similar to how you might when you say "uh oh."

There is also a **kahakō**, which is a line over a letter. For those letters, you hold the sound a little longer.

• •

A E I O U H K L M N P W '

How many everyday English words can you make with just these letters?

kelp

we

SNORKELING
A FUNNY NAME FOR A FUN ACTIVITY

If you want to swim with the fish, or just observe them from above, you should try snorkeling! That's what it's called when you swim on the surface of the water or just below it, wearing a snorkel (a curved tube that lets you breathe as you look), a diving mask (so you can see clearly underwater, and look at the fish), and swim fins (to help you swim smoothly and easily).
Color in the snorkeling equipment below!

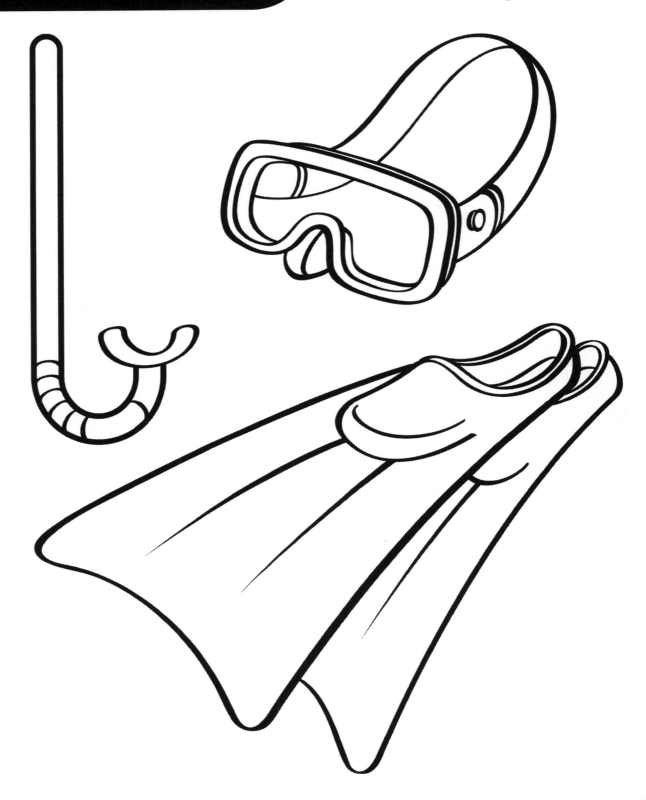

Hawaii's official state fish is the Reef Triggerfish.

Its Hawaiian name, humuhumunukunukuāpua'a, seems like it would be hard to say, but is actually pronounced just like it's spelled, with an emphasis on every other syllable. So you'd say HOO-moo-HOO-moo-NOO-koo-NOO-koo-AH-poo-AH-ah. Since it's such a long word, Hawaiians sometimes refer to them simply as "humu" or "humuhumu."

So what does the name mean? The first part (humuhumu) is Hawaiian for "triggerfish," and the second part means "snout like a pig." In fact, these triggerfishes are known to grunt like pigs if they are pulled out of the water.

Another Hawaiian triggerfish is also called humuhumunukunukuāpua'a — the lagoon triggerfish (also known as the Picasso triggerfish).

Another interesting fact: these brightly-colored tropical fish can swim backwards and forwards.

HUMUHUMUNUKUNUKUĀPUA'A

Some inmformation provided by the National Ocean Service/NOAA

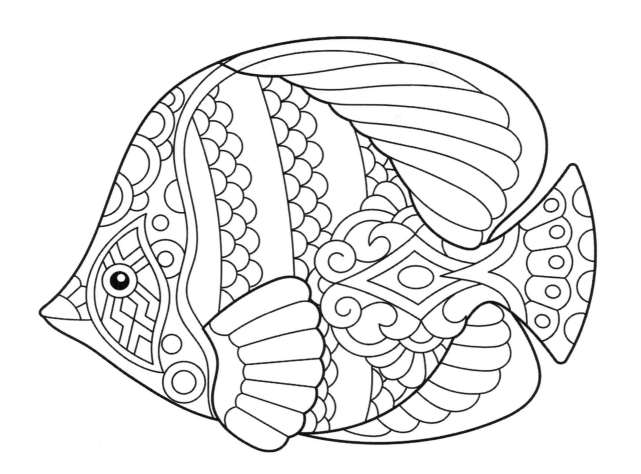

BUTTERFLYFISH

SEE
SEA
SHELLS

COWRIE SHELLS

When you find dozens of them on the beach in Hawaii, you may be surprised to hear that cowrie shells — small versions of those shown here — were once used as money!

For thousands of years, and up until the twentieth century, these little shells were used as one form of payment on several different continents.

Some of the reasons for using the cowries included that they were sturdy, conveniently-sized, easy to identify, and simple to count.

They were so popular, in fact, that for generations, these little smooth and glossy shells from sea snails (mollusks) came to symbolize wealth and power.

HAWAIIAN PLACES

HERE ARE THE NAMES OF
THE MAIN HAWAIIAN ISLANDS
AND SOME OF THE LARGEST
CITIES ON THOSE ISLANDS.
CAN YOU FIND THEM ALL?

PLACES TO FIND

NIIHAU

KAUAI

OAHU

MAUI

MOLOKAI

LANAI

KAHOOLAWE

HONOLULU

HILO

KAHULUI

KIHEI

LIHUE

LAHAINA

KAILUA

WAIPAHU

See solutions starting on page 125

T	H	Y	N	B	D	T	U	I	D	T	W
K	Q	Z	F	G	B	K	A	A	N	L	N
L	A	H	A	I	N	A	H	N	F	F	L
B	R	H	R	L	F	K	I	A	T	L	X
M	L	K	U	K	N	D	I	L	M	Z	W
H	I	L	O	L	A	E	N	R	O	F	A
T	K	J	M	M	U	I	P	K	L	D	I
T	A	V	V	H	Y	I	L	Z	O	T	P
L	H	K	I	O	A	H	U	U	K	V	A
C	O	L	F	D	K	C	L	B	A	M	H
D	O	W	J	X	M	U	R	L	I	Y	U
I	L	K	R	C	L	A	G	W	I	J	M
E	A	X	F	O	G	N	U	A	Z	W	J
H	W	J	N	T	B	Z	U	I	N	L	P
I	E	O	Q	J	J	A	D	H	H	X	Y
K	H	R	K	G	K	L	F	N	F	C	L

Information courtesy NPS/NOAA

CORAL

Corals are small and often colorful plankton-eating animals that are similar to anemones.

Hidden beneath the ocean, coral reefs are filled with life. Reefs are complex structures built by coral and algae, usually in shallow tropical waters.

Each single coral animal is called a polyp, but the coral branches you see on a reef is actually not a single animal, but a huge colony of hundreds or thousands of tiny polyps living side by side!

Fish, lobsters, shrimp, clams, seahorses, sea turtles and sponges are only a few of the thousands of creatures that rely on coral reefs for their survival.

23

HIBISCUS

Flowers of Hawaii

PLUMERIA

(also known as frangipani)

Quilt patterns

Can you finish drawing the other halves of these five Hawaiian quilt-style designs?

Hawaiian quilt-style patterns like these have
been used for well over a hundred years.
The stencil designs on these two pages are just a
few of many such patterns, which are typically used
with a color to contrast with a white background.
Color in the flower and leaf design below!

DRAW! DOODLE! PLAY A GAME!

PAPAYA

PINEAPPLE

GUAVA

MANGO

COCONUT

TROPICAL FRUITS

LYCHEE

JACKFRUIT

MANGOSTEEN

6 FOODS POPULAR IN HAWAII THAT YOU MIGHT NOT KNOW ABOUT

SAIMIN & SPAM MUSUBI NOODLE MAZE PUZZLE

Which noodle in this saimin (noodle soup) leads to the Spam musubi — a piece of grilled Spam meat on top of a block of rice, with dried seaweed (nori) wrapped around it?

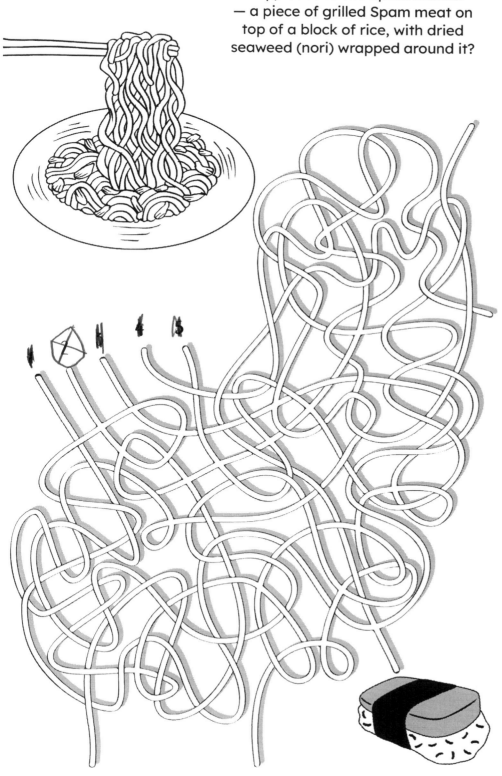

PLATE LUNCH
(Hawaiian: pā mea 'ai)
This is a plate or to-go box with macaroni salad, scoops of white rice, and a protein main dish (such as teriyaki beef, chicken katsu, or kalua pork).

LOCO MOCO
Served for lunch or dinner, the basic version of loco moco has white rice under a seasoned hamburger patty, topped with a fried egg, and is served with brown gravy.

POI
Poi (rhymes with 'boy') is a traditional Hawaiian food made from the taro plant. The taro root is cooked then mashed, and some water is added to give it a paste-like texture. Poi is often purple, and tastes sweet when fresh, but gets sour as it ferments. This ancient dish is popular with both kids and adults in Hawaii.

KALUA PORK
Traditional Kalua pig (or Kalua pork) is a meat served at luaus, and is made by smoking a whole pig in a sand pit dug in the ground.

DANCES IN HAWAII

FIRE

Fire dancing (also called "fire spinning") is based on an ancient art form invented by the people of another Polynesian island called Samoa. Along with hula dancers, you might see these spectacular traditional fire dancers perform at a Hawaiian luau, usually moving to the beat of loud, rhythmic drumming.

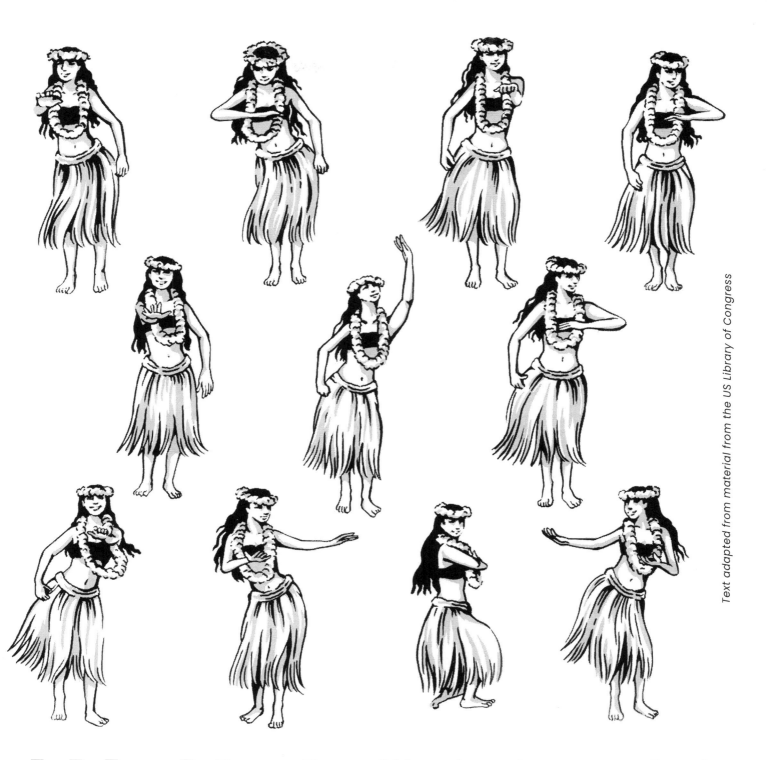

Text adapted from material from the US Library of Congress

HULA

Did you know that you can tell stories with a dance? That's what the people are doing when they do the hula, a traditional dance of Hawaii. The hula combines flowing movement with facial expressions, all set to special chants and music. To many Hawaiians, the hula shows their view of the world.

BIRD OF PARADISE

Flowers of Hawaii

ORCHID

CAN YOU SPOT 10 DIFFERENCES?

PARASAILING

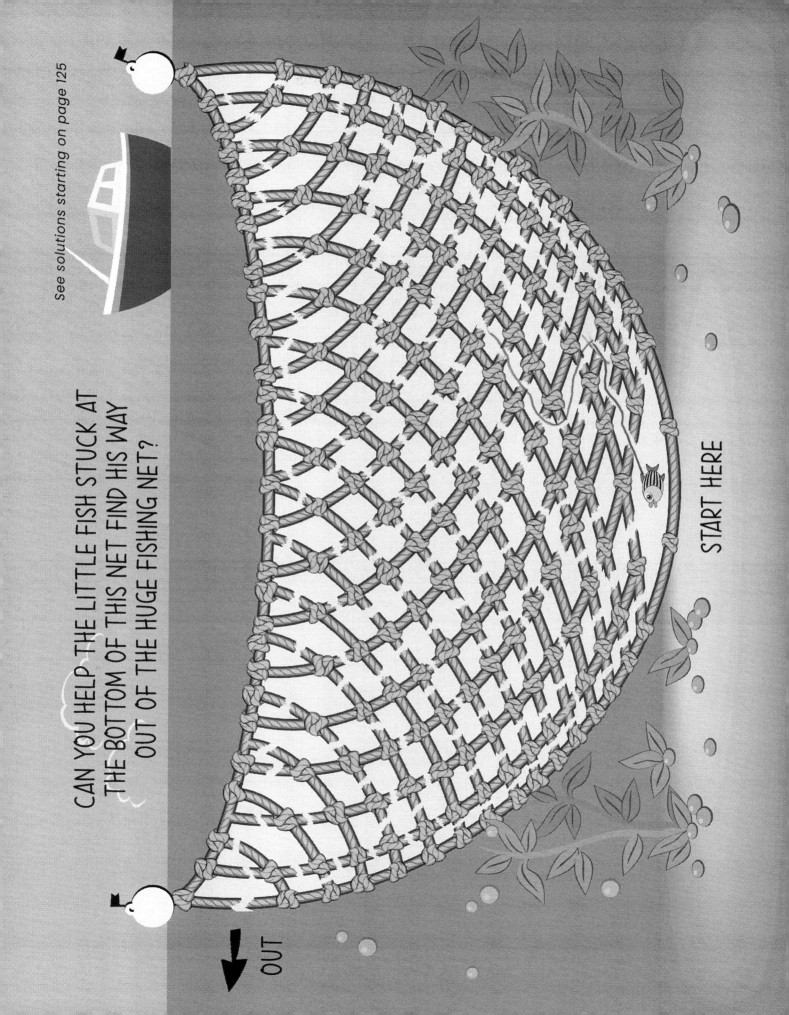

See solutions starting on page 125

CAN YOU HELP THE LITTLE FISH STUCK AT THE BOTTOM OF THIS NET FIND HIS WAY OUT OF THE HUGE FISHING NET?

START HERE

OUT

Make an aloha shirt

One of the most popular items of clothing for people visiting the islands is something called an "aloha shirt." They're usually button-down short-sleeve shirts with a big and colorful Hawaiian-themed pattern all over it. Come up with an idea for your own shirt here! A few pattern ideas are shown at the bottom of the page.

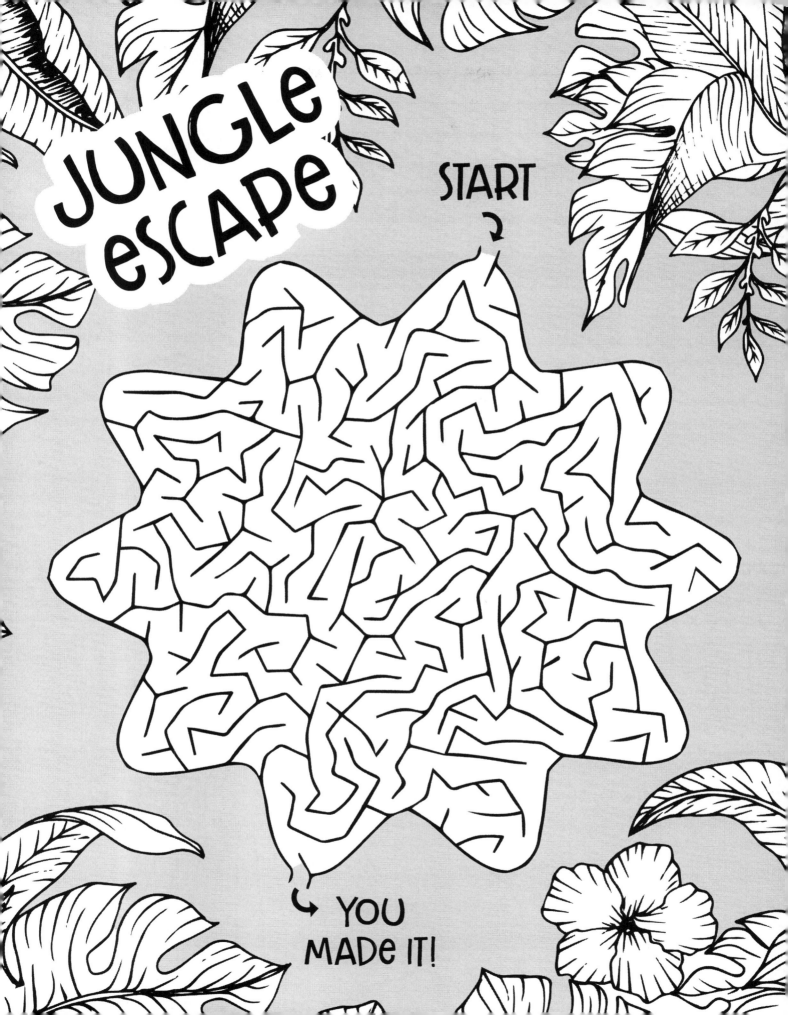

pineapple

sugar cane
used to make sugar

bananas

5 big crops
Here are five famous Hawaiian plants that the rest of the USA - and the world - gets to enjoy.

macadamia nuts

(Not shown to scale)

coffee

Some text provided by the US Library of Congress

OUTRIGGER CANOES

It is believed that the ancient Polynesian people discovered Hawaii around the year 400 A.D. — that's about 1600 years ago.

They traveled in outrigger canoes, navigating the seas for thousands of miles from islands deep in the eastern Pacific Ocean.

The "outrigger" is a beam attached to the side of the boat, to give it extra stability. Often, two canoes were attached together before making long voyages.

When there was wind, the canoes used sails, otherwise, people paddled the craft. Trained navigators carefully watched the positions of the stars and the planets in the night sky to guide their way.

Traditional Hawaiian canoes were historically built by master craftsmen who oversaw all aspects of the process, from selecting the koa tree logs, to getting the vessel on the water.

There were two main types of canoe: the outrigger, and the double-hulled canoe.

Canoes helped early Hawaiians in many different ways. Small canoes were used for traveling around the islands; larger canoes were used for long-distance traveling or for warfare. Fishing was also done with canoes.

But it wasn't all about work! These little boats were also great to have for sports competitions, relaxation and recreation, which is how they are often used today.

PARROT

This is a macaw — a popular type of parrot originally found in tropical areas of North and South America.

They're not native to Hawaii, but you will probably see a few tame ones in tourist areas. You may even have the chance to let one or more of the birds perch on your shoulders while someone takes a picture for you to buy!

The Nēnē, or Hawaiian Goose, is the rarest goose in the world — and is found only in Hawaii. It has been the State Bird since 1959.

Nēnē evolved from Canada geese that by chance flew across the Pacific Ocean, and settled in Hawaii about half a million years ago. Since then, these birds have learned how to live mostly on land.

SEA ANIMALS
CROSSWORD PUZZLE

DIRECTIONS: IN EACH ROW, WRITE THE NAMES OF THE SEA CREATURES SHOWN BELOW! (WE HAVE DONE ONE FOR YOU.) WHEN YOU'RE FINISHED, READ THE LETTERS IN THE SHADED COLUMN IN THE MIDDLE TO SEE SOMEWHERE BESIDES THE OCEAN THAT SEA ANIMALS LIKE THESE CAN BE FOUND!

7. MOLLUSK

See solutions starting on page 125

48

4X4 PICTURE SUDOKU

In these sudoku puzzle games, the goal is to fill in each 4x4 grid with
just one of every picture in each row (sideways) and column (up and down).
Game #1 below shows you an example of a completed sudoku picture grid.
See if you can complete games 2, 3 and 4 on your own!

GAME #1

GAME #2

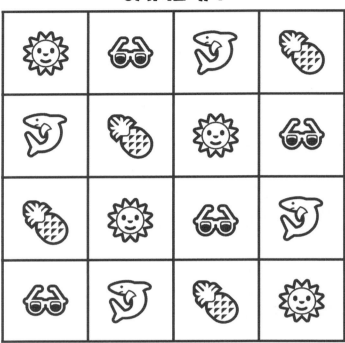

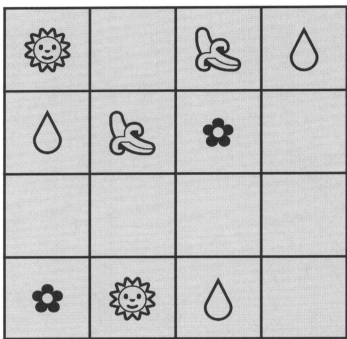

GAME #3

GAME #4

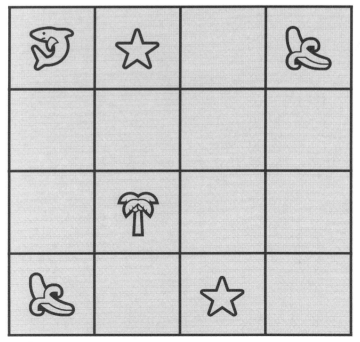

🌴 5X5 PICTURE SUDOKU ☀

In the sudoku puzzle games on this page, you need to fill in each 5x5 grid with only one of every picture in each row (sideways) and column (up and down). After you have mastered these, try making your own grids!

GAME #5

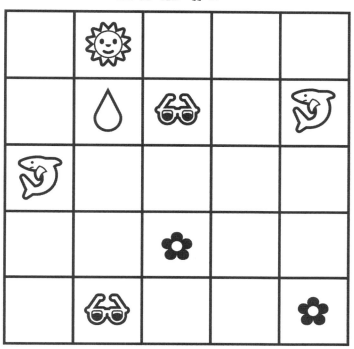

GAME #6

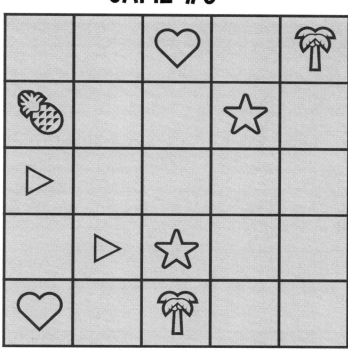

GAME #7

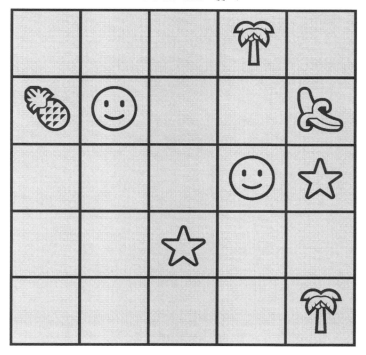

GAME #8

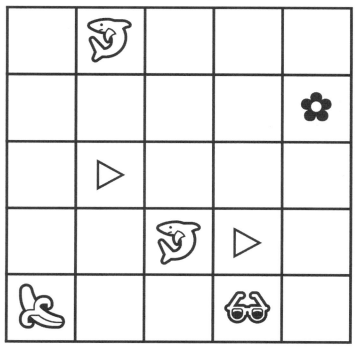

DRAW! DOODLE! PLAY A GAME!

10 DIFFERENCES

THERE ARE 10 DIFFERENCES BETWEEN THE TOP AND THE BOTTOM PICTURES. CAN YOU SPOT THEM ALL?

See solutions starting on page 125

WHICH OF THE NUMBERED BUGS HERE...

 **1**

 **2**

 **3**

 **4**

 **5**

 **6**

 **7**

 **8**

 **9**

...CAN'T BE FOUND ON THE PICTURE HERE?

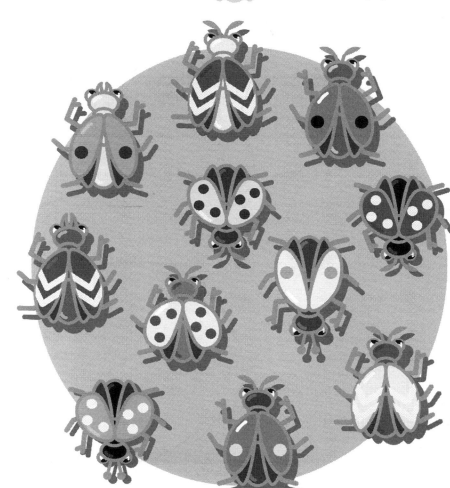

See solutions starting on page 125

TREASURE DIVER

Can you help the diver on the upper left swim to the treasure chest — making sure they avoid the anglerfish, shark and octopus? (Those dangers are marked with dotted circles.)

How many different routes can you find? What is the shortest way? Which is the longest path? And can you find the humuhumunukunukuāpua'a? (If you don't know what that is, you can find out on another page in this book!

SEA TURTLE

dot to dot to dot

Connect the dots to complete this picture,
then color it in! (Hint: You'll need a lot of orange.)

HOW TO DRAW A FISH

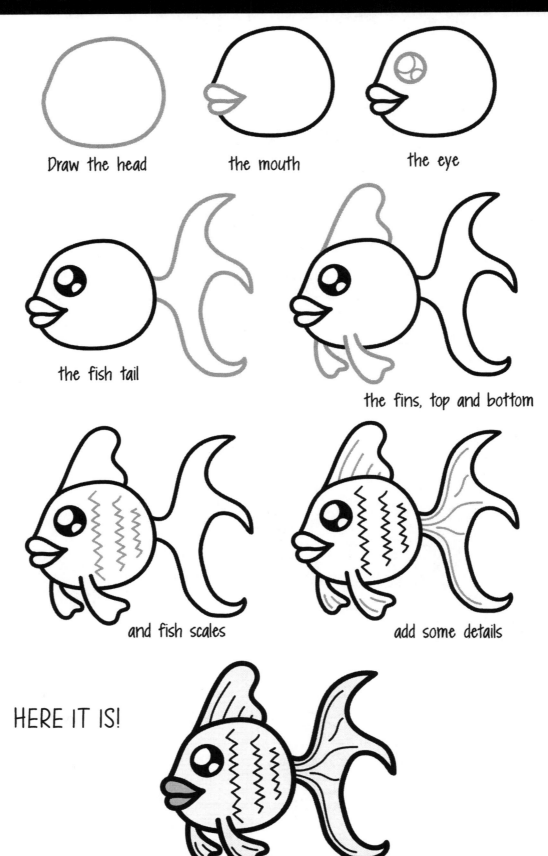

Draw the head

the mouth

the eye

the fish tail

the fins, top and bottom

and fish scales

add some details

HERE IT IS!

NOW YOU DRAW A FISH

GO FISH

WORDSEARCH PUZZLE

```
    M P D L O E R
  E G V B T M O A F
  P H K M S A R D I N E
J T H E K A N M W M C C A
M L Y S D R K H X Z R M H F R
E P N N K Z R T I E N S N M C
Y A W A Q J Y I D M I T Y T A
I G J P M N D N N F A M C E W
M E G P T Y U H L G V H K V B
O Z O E N O R E F F U P I L R
S U B R L L G G F T N F J O Z
Q Y F X N M W R A S S E B
  J X A A N U T G F M M
    Y E V I F O H L T
      I C B W K A S
```

HERRING
ANGELFISH
FLOUNDER
GOBY
MAHIMAHI
PUFFER
WRASSE
SARDINE
SNAPPER
TUNA

See solutions starting on page 125

DOLPHIN

10 DiFFeReNCeS

THERE ARE TEN
DIFFERENCES
BETWEEN THE
TOP AND THE
BOTTOM JELLYFISH
PICTURES.
CAN YOU SPOT
THEM ALL?

See solutions starting on page 125

JELLYFISH

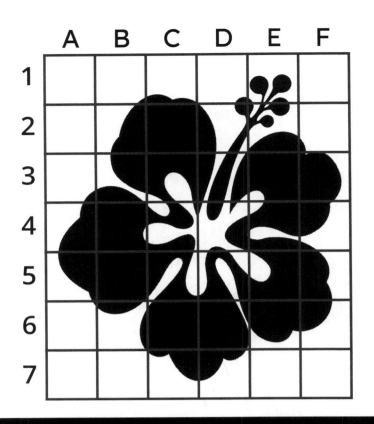

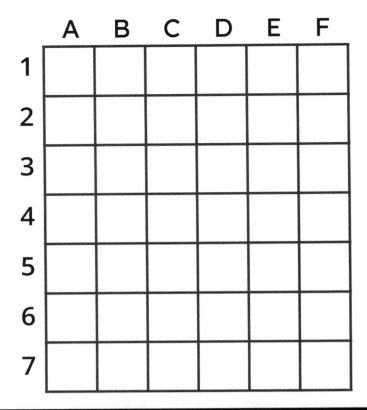

COPY THESE PICTURES
USING THE GRIDS AS YOUR GUIDE
YOU CAN MAKE BIGGER VERSIONS ON A PIECE OF PLAIN PAPER. DRAW
THE GRIDS LIGHTLY WITH PENCIL BEFORE MAKING YOUR COPY.

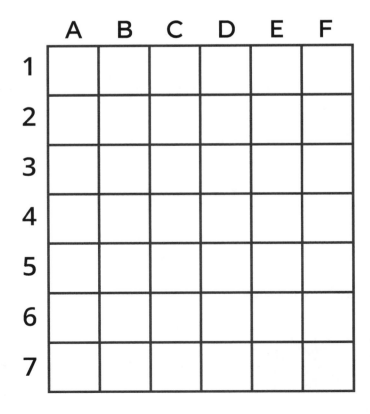

UKULELE

The ukulele may look like a little guitar, but this small stringed instrument plays a big part in the sound of a lot of Hawaiian music!

Although a lot of people outside of Hawaii say its name like "you-koo-lay-lee," in the islands, they pronounce it more like "ooh-koo-lay-lay."

WHICH PIECE ON THE LEFT IS NOT PART OF THIS SNOWFLAKE?

WHICH PIECE ON THE LEFT IS MISSING FROM THIS SNOWFLAKE?

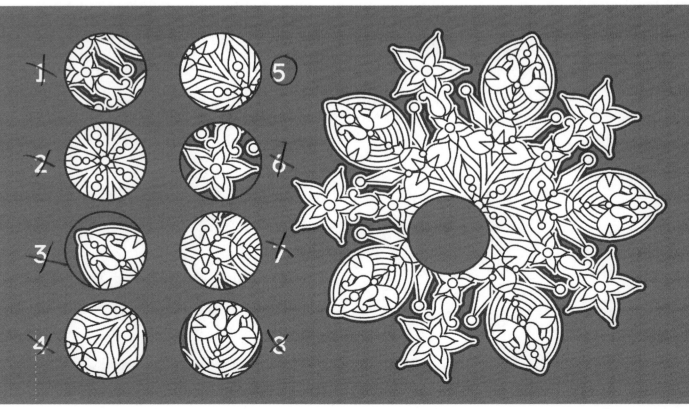

HAWAIIAN SNOW?

When you imagine the weather in Hawaii, you probably don't think about it snowing. But it happens! Find out more at the end of this maze.

START HERE

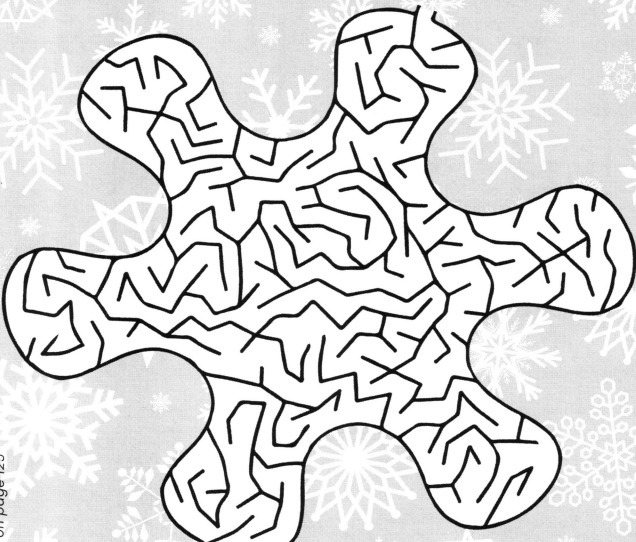

THE END

Information source: NASA Earth Observatory

See solutions starting on page 125

With summits of 13,792 feet and 13,674 feet, it's not unusual for the Mauna Kea (north) and Mauna Loa (south) volcanoes on Hawaii's Big Island to get wintertime snowfall. Now there's not a lot of the white stuff — the islands get an average of 3.7 inches per year.

Long before explorers from Europe first visited the islands, Hawaii was home to thousands of people, and had a strong and vibrant culture all its own.

For many years, the islands of Hawaii were ruled by separate chiefs (seen above).

In 1810, one of these kings — named Kamehameha I — joined the islands into one kingdom, and set himself up as the first king of all Hawaii.

Although King Kamehameha died in 1819, he is still admired for having been the strongest Hawaiian ruler, and for making sure that the kingdom of Hawaii stayed independent for many years.

The famous statue of the king, shown at the right, stands in downtown Honolulu, on the isand of Oahu.

KING KAMEHAMEHA

KAMEHAMEHA I

5 WAYS TO READ & WRITE "HAWAII"

On a separate piece of paper or on one of the blank doodle pages in this book, try out one or more of these different ways to write out the name of America's 50th state!

"HAWAII" IN AMERICAN SIGN LANGUAGE LETTERS

"HAWAII" IN BRAILLE LETTERING

"HAWAII" IN SEMAPHORE FLAGS

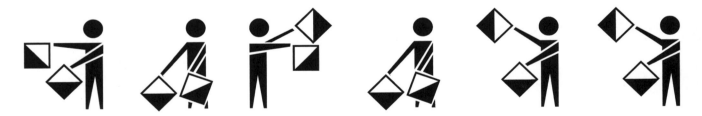

"HAWAII" IN MORSE CODE

"HAWAII" IN MASONIC (PIG PEN) CIPHER

PALM PAIRS

EVERY TREE HERE HAS A MIRROR-IMAGE MATCH. CAN YOU PAIR THEM ALL UP?

Humpback whales have plate-like bristles known as baleen in their mouth instead of teeth. They feed on krill and small fish that swim together (in "schools"), like capelin and herring.

These amazing sea creatures can often be seen in Hawaii during winter, and their impressive acrobatic displays are often visible from miles away! Hawaii is the only state in the U.S. where humpback whales have calves (baby whales) as well as raise their families.

Humpback whales are often called "gentle giants," because these large mammals glide slowly and gracefully while underwater.

HUMPBACK WHALES

SAVE THE WHALES
The humpback whale is endangered. Through an international ban on commercial whaling and legal protections, there are now more than 21,000 North Pacific humpback whales, and more than 10,000 of them visit Hawaii in the winter!

WHALE SONGS
Although many species of whales are vocal, humpback whales are best known for their songs. The "humpback song" consists of sound sequences repeated over and over in a pattern.

Text adapted from material by the National Ocean Service, part of the National Oceanic and Atmospheric Administration (NOAA)

Whale Tails

The tail of a humpback whale — called the fluke — is unique to each whale. Scientists can actually identify each individual whale by looking at the shape of the fluke, the colors, scars, and other marks that are visible. Below, you can try! Match the 12 humpback-style flukes on the top with the same flukes on the bottom.

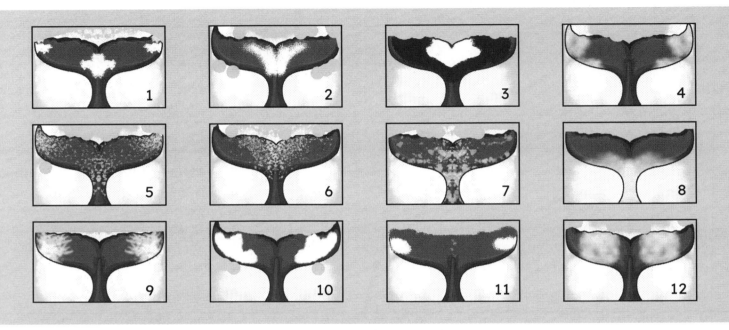

Match up the numbered flukes above with the lettered tails below!

1   2   3   4   5   6   7   8   9   10   11   12

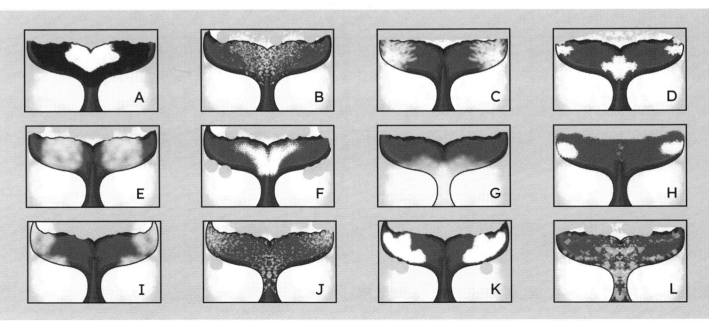

REACH THE BEACH

By staying on the path and using the bridges, can you find your way from the top of the garden down to the beach?

START HERE >

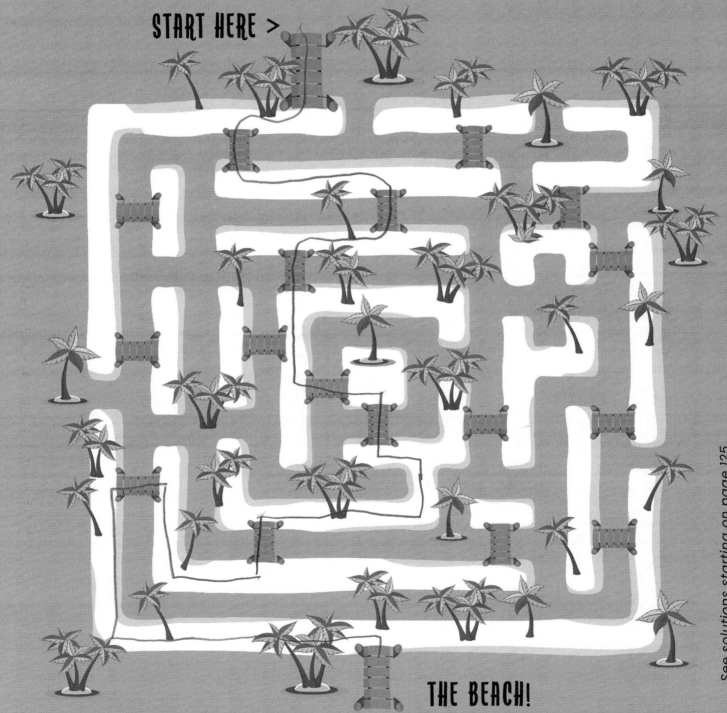

THE BEACH!

See solutions starting on page 125

WISH UPON A STARFISH

WATER IN THE OCEAN

HOW MUCH WATER IS IN THE OCEAN? The National Oceanic and Atmospheric Administration estimates that Earth's seas hold about 321,003,271 cubic miles of water (a cubic mile is the volume of a cube that is one mile long on each side). In everyday terms, that's roughly 352,670,000,000,000,000,000 (three hundred fifty two quintillion, six hundred seventy quadrillion) gallons!

THE GECKO

Geckos have been in Hawaii since the ancient Polynesians first arrived on those shores. They were probably stowaways on the voyaging canoes!

Geckos have big toes and specialized hairs on their feet called *setae* that let them stick to walls and ceilings without falling. (You can see their footprints below.)

The gecko can be noisy! Its call seems loud for such a small lizard creature, and can sound like a croak or a kind of chirp.

Geckos love to eat live insects, and so help keep a lot of bugs away, such as ants, roaches and crickets. We're lucky to have them!

natural wonders

AHCEB _ _ _ _ _

AOONVCL _ _ _ _ _ _ _

CNOEA _ _ _ _ _

ETUNSS _ _ _ _ _ _

FIFCL _ _ _ _ _

KYS _ _ _

LALYVE _ _ _ _ _ _

NEJGUL _ _ _ _ _ _

RLLTAFWEA _ _ _ _ _ _ _ _ _

TMANIUON _ _ _ _ _ _ _ _

See solutions starting on page 125

WHICH TWO BUTTERFLIES ARE THE SAME?

84

THE HAWAIIAN MONK SEAL
IS HAWAII'S STATE MAMMAL

SURF'S UP IN HAWAII!

HAWAII IS CONSIDERED TO BE THE BIRTHPLACE OF SURFING – SOMETHING THAT ANCIENT HAWAIIANS USED TO CALL "HE'E NALU", WHICH MEANS "WAVE SLIDING."

The ancient art of wave sliding has evolved to include big wave charging, barrel riding, and amazing stunts in the air.

As you can probably imagine, the Hawaiian islands also have some of the best surfing in the world! Two major hotspots for professional surfers are both located on the island of Oahu's North Shore, and are called Banzai and Waimea.

BANZAI PIPELINE

Known simply as "Pipeline," or just "Pipe," this famous spot on Oahu's North Shore draws world-class surfers every winter with its towering swells and picture-perfect barrels. The waves break over a shallow reef, making Banzai one of the most powerful (and most dangerous) surf spots in the world.

WAIMEA BAY

As home to professional surfing tournaments, Oahu's beautiful Waimea Bay was one of the first big wave surfing destinations to gain international fame.

Text adapted from material provided by the NOAA's Office of National Marine Sanctuaries

SURFING, USA

HERE ARE 8 SURFBOARDS
THAT NEED SOME COLOR!

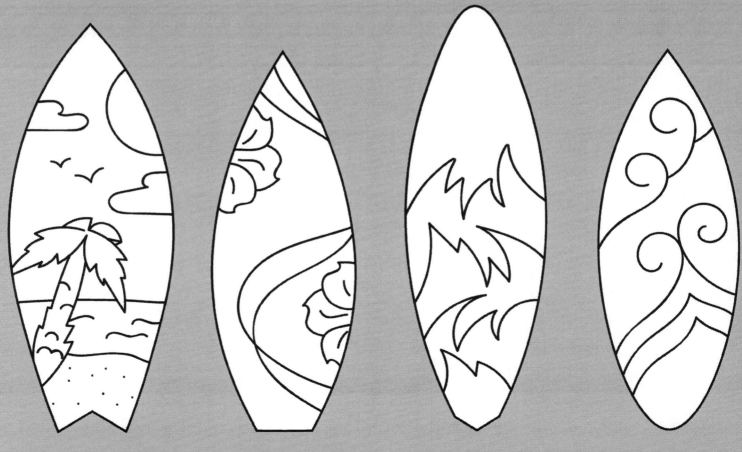

SURF BADGES

The hand gesture shown on the left is the shaka sign, otherwise known as "hang loose." It's a very common friendly gesture in Hawaii, with several similar meanings — thanks, relax, all good, cool.

COCONUTS & VOLCANOES

AN EASY & FUN DOT GAME

Perfect for a long flight! In this variation of the classic dots game, one player's symbol is a coconut (a circle or O) and the other player's symbol is a volcano (a triangle or upside-down V).

The two players take turns adding a single line (horizontal or vertical) between two unjoined dots that are next to each other on the game board. Points are earned by completing the fourth side of a square. The player who completes a box puts their symbol inside the square (as shown below) to track their points and gets another turn.

When no more lines can be drawn, the winner is the player with the most points. Five boards are here, and you can also make your own!

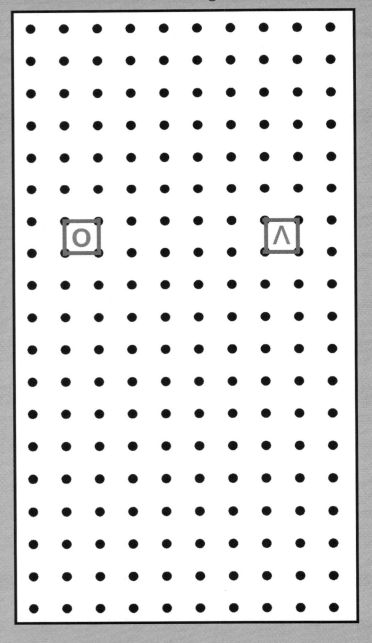

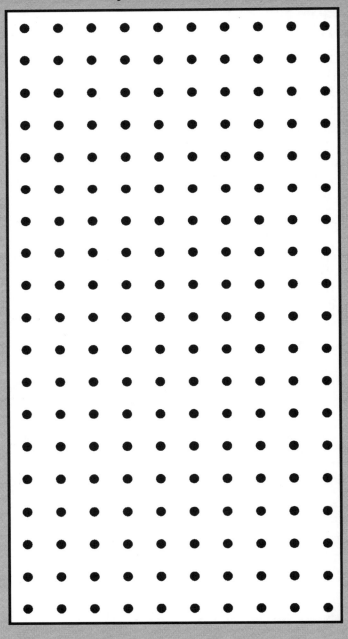

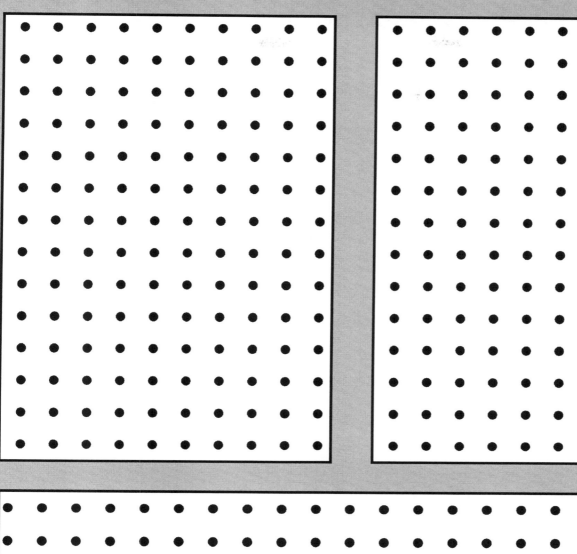

DRAW! DOODLE! PLAY A GAME!

STAIRS TO THE SHORE MAZE

START HERE

THE SHORE!

See solutions starting on page 125

PADDLEBOARDING
ALSO CALLED STAND UP PADDLE (SUP) BOARDING

VOLCANOES

Kilauea Volcano is a shield volcano located on the eastern slope of Mauna Loa Volcano on the Island of Hawaii.

Towering lava fountains, likely more than 2,000 feet high, roared from the Kilauea caldera just after it formed, and began 300 years of explosive eruptions that ended in the early 19th century.

In 1959, lava burst from a crack in the crater wall; then multiple vents merged producing a giant fountain of lava that radiated up to 1,900 feet, taller than the Empire State Building, and among the highest ever recorded on Kilauea!

The spectacular event lasted five weeks. Molten rock flooded the crater, creating a lake that rose up the crater walls. The winds blew and carried cinder to the edge of the crater. Many trees were buried under 20 feet of cinder, and leaves of other trees were stripped from their branches leaving them looking like a forest of skeletons. The rainforest is still recovering and reclaiming the land burned by this eruption.

Imagine the roar of lava blasting skyward! A deep rumble was heard from far away, long before people were close enough to see the lava fountains.

The current eruption of Kilauea Volcano began in 1983 with spectacular lava fountaining at a new vent high on the volcano's east rift zone. Although surface flows have been common, most of the lava from the vent travels concealed in lava tubes until it reaches the ocean.

When lava moves through the landscape and into the ocean, we see how the islands are created.

The experience of witnessing rock in its bright molten state and watching land being formed has fascinated and inspired countless people over the centuries.

Information courtesy of the National Parks Service and the US Geological Survey

MARS OR MAUI?

Three of the pictures below were taken on planet earth — in or above one of Hawaii's volcanic craters on the island of Maui — and the other three photos were taken by NASA on the planet Mars. Can you tell which is which?

#1

#2

#3

#4

#5

#6

See solutions starting on page 125

1:          2:   3:   4:   5:   6:

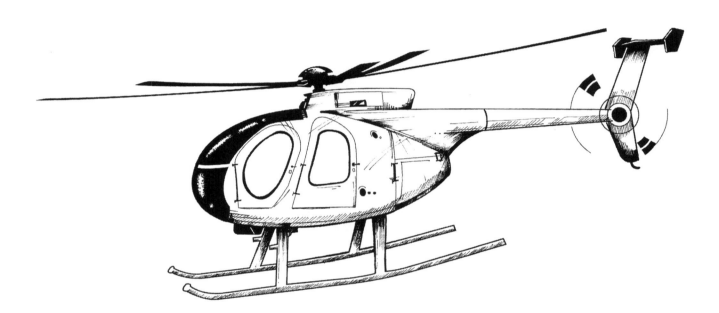

HOP ON A HELICOPTER

There are lots of incredible helicopter tours in Hawaii, making it possible to see
the mountains, volcanoes, cliffs, waterfalls — and even whales — in a whole new way!
On this page, draw what you wish you could see on a "chopper" ride.

FLYING WORDS

Try to find all 12 of these plane-related words in the puzzle below!
Words can go across, backwards, down and diagonally.
When you are done, the unused letters in the grid will spell out a hidden message.
Pick them out from left to right, top line to bottom line.

AIRPLANE	BOARDING	LANDING	TAKEOFF
AIRPORT	CARRYON	SEATS	TICKET
AISLE	FLIGHT	SUITCASE	TRAYTABLE

See solutions starting on page 125

T	L	H	A	S	E	A	T	S	E	V	G
E	A	A	C	W	O	N	D	N	E	N	R
F	N	K	F	A	U	L	A	V	I	A	S
L	D	C	E	A	R	L	T	D	I	O	U
I	I	N	I	O	P	R	R	N	H	A	I
G	N	W	A	R	F	A	Y	I	I	T	T
H	G	T	I	E	O	F	Z	O	W	W	C
T	K	A	L	B	W	K	Q	T	N	Q	A
F	D	S	L	N	T	E	K	C	I	T	S
R	I	L	A	I	R	P	O	R	T	F	E
A	P	E	L	B	A	T	Y	A	R	T	J

CODED MESSAGE: _ _ _ _ _   _   _ _ _ _ _ _ _ _ _

_ _ _ _ _ _ _ _   _ _   _ _ _ _ _ _

COLOR YOUR PLANE TO HAWAII

CAN YOU FIND THE FOUR BAGS (OR SUITCASE STACKS) THAT ARE INCLUDED TWICE?

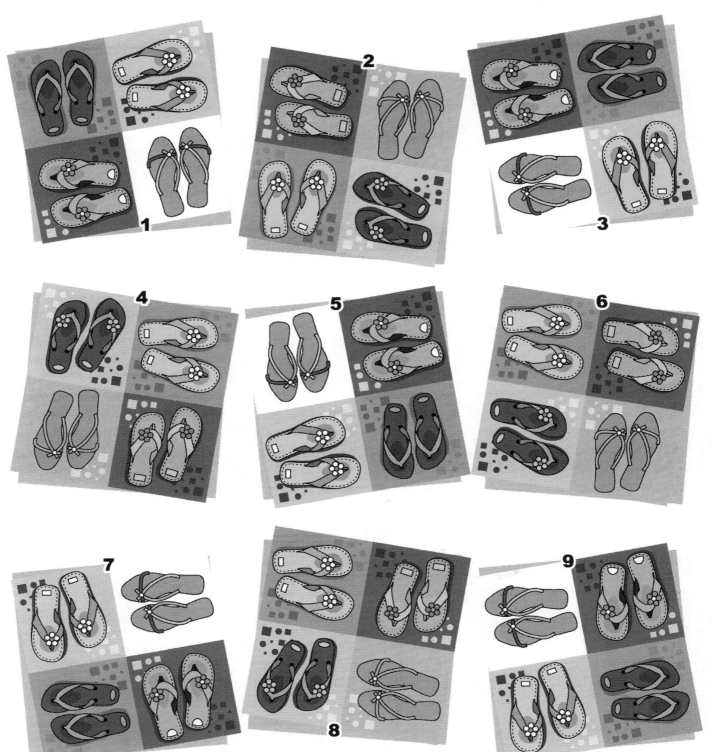

See solutions starting on page 125

FLiPPED FLiP FLOPS

WHICH TWO IMAGES OF THESE FLIP-FLOP SHOES ARE THE SAME? (HINT: THE PICTURE MAY HAVE BEEN ROTATED.)

READY TO PACK?

FIND THESE THINGS

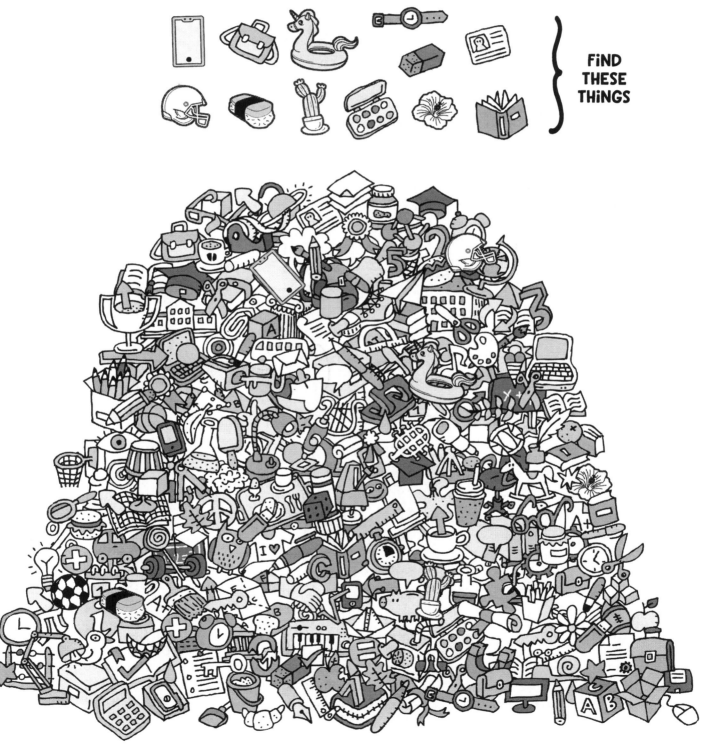

START HERE

PACK YOUR SUITCASE!

LET'S GO!

See solutions starting on page 125

ON THE PAGES AHEAD:

PACKING LISTS
A VISUAL GUIDE TO WHAT YOU MIGHT WANT TO BRING ALONG WITH YOU, PLUS ONE DOUBLE-SIDED SHEET TO LIST EVERYTHING YOU NEED

LITTLE PLAN LISTS
8 LITTLE LISTS WHERE YOU CAN KEEP TRACK OF ALL THE THINGS YOU PLAN FOR HAWAII: PLACES TO GO, THINGS TO SEE, STUFF TO DO, WHAT TO FIND, ETC.

TRAVEL JOURNAL
11 PAGES FOR YOU TO KEEP A RECORD OF YOUR AMAZING VACATION IN WORDS, DRAWINGS, PHOTOS AND ANYTHING ELSE YOU WANT TO ADD.
THE JOURNAL PAGES CAN ALSO BE REMOVED AND SAVED SEPARATELY.

PICTURE YOUR PACKING LIST

The best way to make sure you bring along everything you need is to make a list ahead of time. To make it easier, on the next page are blank lists to fill out! As you pack each item, check it off on the list. Below are ideas for a few items you might think about taking along to Hawaii. (Be sure to leave some space in your bags for anything you get and want to bring home.)

LIST FOR TRAVEL BAG (CARRY-ON)

☐ ....
☐ ....
☐ ....
☐ ....
☐ ....
☐ ....
☐ ....

☐ ....
☐ ....
☐ ....
☐ ....
☐ ....
☐ ....
☐ ....

LIST FOR MAIN SUITCASE/BACKPACK

☐ ....
☐ ....
☐ ....
☐ ....
☐ ....
☐ ....
☐ ....
☐ ....
☐ ....
☐ ....
☐ ....
☐ ....
☐ ....

☐ ....
☐ ....
☐ ....
☐ ....
☐ ....
☐ ....
☐ ....

TRAVEL OUTFIT

☐ ....
☐ ....
☐ ....
☐ ....

CHECKLIST: THINGS TO GET OR FIND BEFORE YOU GO

- [ ] ....
- [ ] ....
- [ ] ....
- [ ] ....
- [ ] ....
- [ ] ....
- [ ] ....

- [ ] ....
- [ ] ....
- [ ] ....
- [ ] ....
- [ ] ....
- [ ] ....
- [ ] ....

CHECKLIST: THINGS TO DO BEFORE YOUR VACATION

- [ ] ....
- [ ] ....
- [ ] ....
- [ ] ....
- [ ] ....
- [ ] ....
- [ ] ....
- [ ] ....
- [ ] ....
- [ ] ....
- [ ] ....
- [ ] ....
- [ ] ....

- [ ] ....
- [ ] ....
- [ ] ....
- [ ] ....
- [ ] ....
- [ ] ....
- [ ] ....
- [ ] ....
- [ ] ....
- [ ] ....
- [ ] ....
- [ ] ....
- [ ] ....

PLACES TO GO

_____
_____
_____
_____
_____
_____
_____
_____
_____

THINGS TO SEE

_____
_____
_____
_____
_____
_____
_____
_____
_____

THINGS TO DO

_____
_____
_____
_____
_____
_____
_____
_____

STUFF TO FIND

_____
_____
_____
_____
_____
_____
_____
_____

FOODS TO TASTE/EAT

_____
_____
_____
_____
_____
_____
_____
_____
_____
_____
_____

PHOTOS TO TAKE

_____
_____
_____
_____
_____
_____
_____
_____
_____
_____
_____

THINGS TO BUY

_____
_____
_____
_____
_____
_____
_____
_____
_____
_____
_____

_____
_____
_____
_____
_____
_____
_____
_____
_____
_____
_____

Hawaii
travel
journal

Hawaii travel journal

Hawaii travel journal

Hawaii travel journal

Hawaii travel journal

Hawaii travel journal

Hawaii travel journal

Hawaii travel journal

NUMBERED BUGS

1, 5, 7, 8

THINGS TO DO IN HAWAII WORDSEARCH

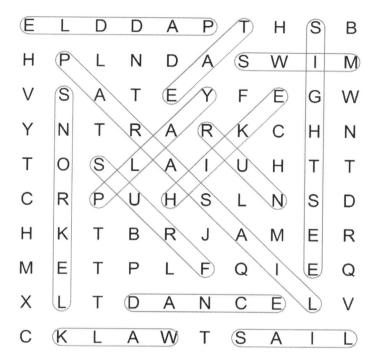

READY TO PACK MAZE

10 DIFFERENCES – SQUID

HAWAIIAN PLACES WORDSEARCH

SOLUTIONS

REACH THE BEACH MAZE

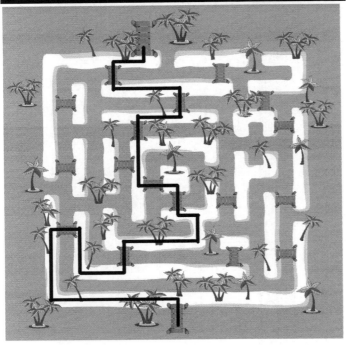

FISHING NET MAZE

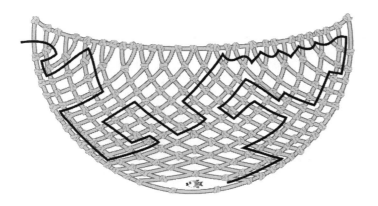

SEA ANIMALS CROSSWORD

1: Seahorse
2: Squid
3: Octopus
4: Starfish
5: Crab

6: Fish
7: Mollusk
8: Shrimp
9: Aquarium

SNOWFLAKE PIECE PUZZLES

TOP: 7; BOTTOM: 4

FLYING WORDS WORDSEARCH

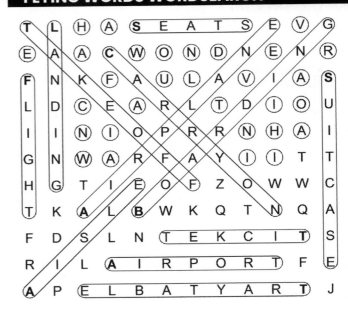

STAIRS TO THE SHORE MAZE

MARS OR MAUI?

1: HAWAII 2: MARS 3: MARS
4: HAWAII 5: HAWAII 6: MARS

Earth images of Maui's Haleakala
Crater courtesy of the National Parks
Service and the US Geological Survey.
Mars images thanks to JPL/NASA.

10 DIFFERENCES – IGUANA

GO FISH WORDSEARCH

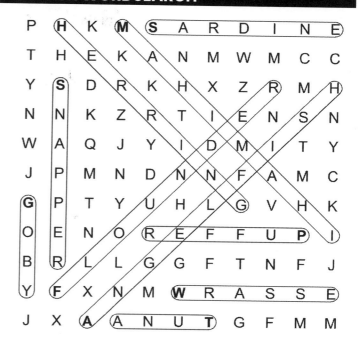

HAWAIIAN SNOW MAZE

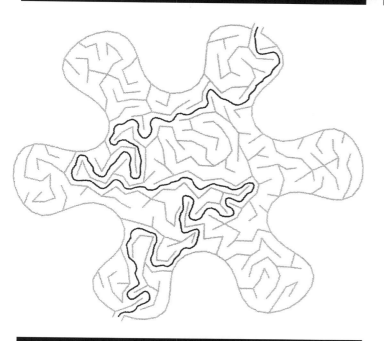

ESCAPE FROM THE JUNGLE MAZE

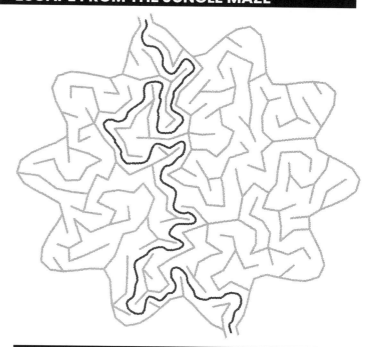

IDENTICAL BUTTERFLIES

4 and 11 are the same

FLIPPED FLIP FLOPS

5 and 7 are the same

NATURAL WONDERS SCRAMBLE

Beach	Sky
Volcano	Valley
Ocean	Jungle
Sunset	Waterfall
Cliff	Mountain

P.S. If you liked this book, please leave a review of it on Amazon. Thank you!

P.P.S. For free coloring pages & more good stuff for kids, visit PrintColorFun.com

PLUS: Take a look back at vintage Hawaii and the USA at ClickAmericana.com